Class

Akbar and Birbal

& Other Stories

Published by

MAPLE PRESS PRIVATE LIMITED
office: A-63, Sector 58, Noida 201301, U.P., India
phone: +91 120 455 3581, 455 3583
email: info@maplepress.co.in
website: www.maplepress.co.in

Reprinted in 2020
Printed and bound in Noida, India

ISBN: 978-93-50335-41-3

Akbar and Birbal

Akbar was a very famous Mughal King. He ruled over India. He was kind and honest with all humans. But, he was also essentially strong. He was so nice and charming, so that his people loved him and his enemies respected him.

Akbar's court had 'navratanas' or the nine gems. Birbal was one among them. Birbal's intelligence and wisdom made him Akbar's favourite. The other courtiers were very jealous of him because Birbal could solve any problem which was given to him.

One day, a sculptor came to Akbar's court with three beautiful statues. The statues looked alike, but from inside their bodies were sculptured in a different manner.

The sculptor presented the statues to the king and said, 'Your Majesty, these statues are alike, but only one of them is the best. Can you ask anyone of your wise men to tell me, which one is the best statue? He should also tell me the reason for his choice'.

Birbal was called to select the best statue. The king said to Birbal, 'You are the most intelligent individual in my court. But, you have to prove your intelligence once again in the court. You have to select the best statue'.

Birbal took the statues in his hands and observed them carefully. He found that there were small holes in the ears and mouths of the statues.

Birbal asked for a long and a thin wire. He took the first statue and inserted the wire into its ear. The wire came out of the statue's mouth.

He picked up the second statue and inserted the wire into its ear. The wire came out of the other ear.

Finally, Birbal took the third statue in his hands. He inserted the wire into its ear. The wire went into the stomach of the statue.

Now, the wise Birbal found the answer. He smiled and pointed to the third statue. He said to the sculptor, 'Though all the statues are alike, this is the best among all the three statues'.

The sculptor was shocked by the answer. He was really surprised that how could Birbal tell the right answer. He asked Birbal, 'Can you tell me why?'

Birbal then answered, 'Let us suppose that each statue is a minister of the king and the wire is a secret of the state. In the first statue, the wire inserted into the ear came out of the mouth. Such a minister will hear a secret and tell it to everybody. He is not a good minister'.

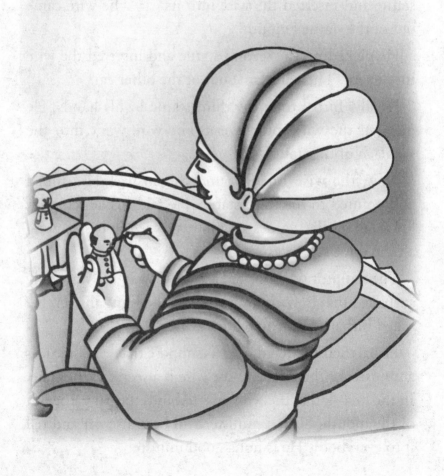

'The wire inserted into the ear of the second statue, came out of the other ear. Such a minister is not worried about the secrets of the state. Whatever he hears with one ear, it leaves out of the other ear. He is also not a good minister'.

'Finally, in the case of the third statue, the wire inserted into the ear went right into the stomach'.

'This is a minister, who hears a secret but never tells it to anyone. He can maintain a secret. He is the best minister. Therefore, this statue is the best among all the three'.

When the king heard this explanation, he became very happy. He thanked God for sending him such a wise and intelligent minister.

Akbar-Tansen

Once upon a time, there was a great Mughal King named Akbar. His court was very famous. He had nine important courtiers in his court. The nine courtiers were together called as the 'navratnas' or the nine gems, and they were very famous.

Tansen was one among the 'navratnas'. He was a very famous singer. Akbar was very proud of Tansen.

One afternoon, Akbar gathered everybody. He then said, 'I have decided to conduct a competition. I invite somebody to come forward and sing against Tansen'.

Everybody knew that Tansen was a very good singer. That is why, nobody wanted to sing against Tansen. Tansen waited for a long time for someone to come forward and sing against him, but nobody came.

Finally, a man wearing torn clothes came forward. His appearance resembled a beggar. He said, 'I will sing against Tansen'. Everybody was really surprised.

Tansen was very happy that someone has come forward to sing against him. He got ready and started singing.

While Tansen was singing, a herd of deer came to the court. They had come because they had liked the music.

Akbar and the people were surprised to see the herd of deer. Tansen took out his garland and put it around one of the deer's neck.

Now, it was the turn of the other man. The other man started singing. Everybody liked his way of singing.

All of a sudden, the same herd of deer came there again. The other man who was singing took off the garland from the deer's neck. Everybody was shocked. They could not believe their eyes. Even Akbar was shocked to see this.

The other man said, 'Now, I will sing a special raag'. He then looked around. Everybody was looking at the other man. He continued, 'The raag will melt the rock. I will then keep my tampura in the rock'.

He again looked around. All the people were waiting for him to say something else. The man then said, 'After the raag is over, the rock will become solid again'.

The man started singing. The raag, which he sung was very nice. Everybody was staring at the rock. Suddenly, the rock started melting. The man kept his tampura in the rock. Then, he finished his raag and the rock became solid again.

Now, even Akbar was sure that this has to be a special man. He looked at Tansen. Tansen got up and went near the man and said, 'You must be Baiju Maharaja. My guru had told me that only Baiju could do this'.

Yes! The man was Baiju Maharaja. Akbar was very happy to see him. Baiju then said to Akbar, 'Please give Tansen the highest position in your court'. Saying this, he left the court.

Sheikh Chilli

Once upon a time, there lived a man named Sheikh Chilli. He was very poor because he did not want to work. He was very lazy. He wanted everything to happen on its own.

Sheikh Chilli wanted to become very rich. But, you know, you cannot become rich, if you do not work hard. Sheikh Chilli used to beg that is why he had only what people gave him.

One day, somebody gave Sheikh Chilli a pot of milk. Sheikh Chilli became very happy. He was so happy that he skipped back home.

He boiled the milk. Then, he put the milk in two separate pots. He drank the milk from the first pot. Then, he added some curd to the second pot. He added the curd so that the milk could be converted into curd.

After adding the curd in the second pot, Sheikh Chilli decided to rest. He lay down on his cot and started dreaming.

As Sheikh Chilli was very happy with the pot of milk, he started dreaming of that milk. He dreamt that the pot of milk has got converted to a pot of curd. And slowly, he has become very rich.

Sheikh Chilli saw that all his problems had solved. He thought, 'In the morning, when I woke, I would make butter out of the curd'.

He dreamt on, 'Then, I would heat the butter and make ghee out of it. I will get a pot full of ghee. Then, I will go to the market and sell the ghee. My ghee would be so nice that everybody would want it'.

Then he thought, 'With the money that I will get I will buy a hen. That hen would lay many eggs. When the eggs would hatch, there would be many more hens. The hens would also lay hundreds of eggs'.

That was not the end of his dream. He then thought, 'With so many hens, I would have my own poultry farm. Then after some time, I will sell all the hens and buy some cows'.

Sheikh Chilli went on dreaming, 'I will have so many cows that I will open a milk dairy. I will sell the milk of the cows. The milk would be so nice that all the people of the town would take milk only from me'.

He still continued to dream, 'If I sell milk to the whole town, I will become very rich. From the money, I will then

buy a lot of jewellery. The jewellery would be so nice that the king would buy the jewellery from me'.

Sheikh Chilli then went on thinking, 'I would be so rich that I will be able to marry a beautiful girl. Soon, I will have a handsome son. We will be really happy'.

Then he thought, 'If somebody would complain about him, then I would hit him with a big stick and teach him a lesson'.

Dreaming this, Sheikh Chilli picked up a stick. He hit the pot with the stick. The pot of milk broke. Sheikh Chilli got up hurriedly and saw that he had only been dreaming.

Alladin in China

Once upon a time, there lived a boy named Aladdin in China. He do not have his father. His mother earned a little money by washing clothes, and so they were very poor.

One day when Aladdin was playing in the street, a strange man with a long beard came up to him and asked, 'Are you Aladdin, the son of Mustafa?'

Aladdin was surprised, and answered, 'Yes, but my father passed away many years ago'.

The man replied, 'Oh! I am sorry to hear that, I wish to help you. Would you like to become rich?' Aladdin answered, 'Yes'. 'Then, follow me', said the stranger.

The stranger who was really a wicked magician took Aladdin to a place in the hills.

He showed him a stone with a ring attached to it and asked him to lift it. Below the stone there was a deep hole with a narrow tunnel.

The magician told Aladdin, 'Jump down and go into the tunnel. At the end of the tunnel is a cave full of gold, silver and gems. Bring me back an old lamp that you will find in a corner. Take this magic ring, it will protect you from harm'.

Aladdin did as he was instructed by the stranger. He found the cave was filled with full of gold, silver and gems, which he had never seen before. He filled his pocket as much as he could and went back through the tunnel.

The magician told him, 'Give me the lamp and I will lift you up'.

Aladdin said, 'No. First lift me up'.

The magician became angry and said, 'Then stay there forever'. And he closed the hole with the stone. Aladdin was really scared and started crying. As he rubbed his eyes, his fingers rubbed the ring which the magician had given him.

In a cloud of smoke, a strange creature appeared and said, 'I am the genie of the ring. What is your desire?'

Aladdin said, 'I want to go home.' Immediately, Aladdin found himself at his home.

He told his mother all that had happened and showed her the lamp. She said, 'How dirty it is!' and started cleaning it with a cloth. There was a light and again a strange creature appeared and said, 'I am the genie of the lamp. What is your desire?'

Aladdin asked for food, clothes and a big house. Instantly, the house they lived in became a pretty cottage with cupboards full of clothes for Aladdin and his mother. In front of them was a table laden with bowls of fruit and plates of delicious food.

From that day onwards, Aladdin and his mother had whatever they desired.

Years passed and Aladdin grew to be a handsome young man. One day, he saw the emperor's daughter and fell in love with her. He gave a gold plate filled with precious stones to his mother and told her, 'Take this to the emperor and tell him that I want to marry his daughter'.

His mother went to the palace and told what Aladdin had said. The emperor was dazzled by the tray of precious stones and agreed to the marriage. Aladdin ordered the genie of the lamp to build him a magnificent palace. He lived there very happily with his princess. Now, the story of Aladdin and his wealth reached the ears of the wicked magician who at once realised that Aladdin must have got the magic lamp.

The wicked magician dressed up as a peddlar and stood outside Aladdin's palace and shouted, 'New lamps for old!' The princess thinking that Aladdin would be happy to see a shinning new one, gave the magic lamp to the peddlar. As soon as he got the lamp, he rubbed it. He asked the genie to carry the palace with the princess and him to Africa.

When Aladdin returned from hunting, he found that his palace and his beloved wife is missing.

He was in a great despair, but he soon realised that this must be the work of the magician.

Aladdin rubbed the magic ring which he still wore and asked the genie of the ring to take him to the princess. In a flash, Aladdin found himself outside his palace.

The princess who was at the window saw him and let him in. Aladdin asked her what had happened.

The princess narrated what had taken place. Aladdin asked her, 'where is the lamp now?' She replied, 'The magician keeps it under his cloak. It never leaves him'.

He gave the princess a packet of sleeping powder and said, 'when you dine with him tonight, add this in his wine'.

While the princess and the magician were dining, she quietly added the sleeping powder in the magician's wine without his knowledge.

When the magician drank the wine, he fell into deep sleep. Then, Aladdin came and took the lamp from under his cloak. He rubbed the lamp and told the genie of the lamp, 'Take us and the palace back to China but leave the magician behind'.

The genie of the lamp carried the palace with the princess and Aladdin inside back to China where they lived happily thereafter.

As for the wicked magician, when he woke up, he found himself all alone in Africa with nothing - the princess, the palace and the lamp had all disappeared.

The Wolf and The Crane

Once a wolf swallowed a bone, which got stuck in his throat.

The pain was unbearable, so the wolf started looking for someone who could help him in exchange for a reward. The wolf asked each of the animals if they would help him. Finally the crane was convinced by the wolf's promises.

Trusting her long beak to the wolf's gaping jaws, the crane carried out the dangerous cure. Yet when the crane demanded the promised reward, the wolf simply said, "You ungrateful creature! You extracted your head unharmed from my mouth and still you ask for a reward?"